Dinosaur
Stories
that
Really Happened

Dinosaur
Stories
that
Really Happened

Andrew Donkin

Illustrated by David Wyatt

For Sophie, with love. xx

Scholastic Children's Books,
Commonwealth House, 1-19 New Oxford Street,
London WC1A 1NU, UK

A division of Scholastic Ltd
London ~ New York ~ Toronto ~ Sydney ~ Auckland
Mexico City ~ New Delhi ~ Hong Kong

Published in the UK by Scholastic Ltd, 2000

ISBN 0 439 01072 1

Typeset by M Rules
Printed and bound by Bath Press, Bath

2 4 6 8 10 9 7 5 3

Contents

Before you begin…

Everyone loves dinosaurs. Perhaps that's because they are the closest thing to real monsters that have ever lived on our planet.

We know about dinosaurs because we can find their bones and other remains today in the form of fossils. I found my first fossil when I was seven years old and I've been collecting them ever since.

Three of the stories in this book are about scientists discovering fantastic fossils. To make them more enjoyable to read, I've made up some of the conversations, but all the stories really happened. The other three stories are set millions of years ago in the age of the dinosaurs. The way the dinosaurs behave in the stories is based on the latest information that scientists have about how they lived, fought, and how they died.

Andrew Park

The Hunt

The Cretaceous period – 70 million years ago

The Tyrannosaurus rex, moving at speed, smashed through the forest of oak trees. Its huge three-toed feet pounded into the forest floor, leaving behind deep footprints.

The Tyrannosaurus rex was the largest and deadliest hunting machine that ever walked the planet. This one was a mature male in the peak of his killing form.

A terrible battle scar ran down one side

of his right leg. The healed white tissue stood out against the surrounding skin.

White Scar crashed through the thick undergrowth as he got closer to the kill. The giant beast was hungry. He hadn't eaten for days – but that was about to change.

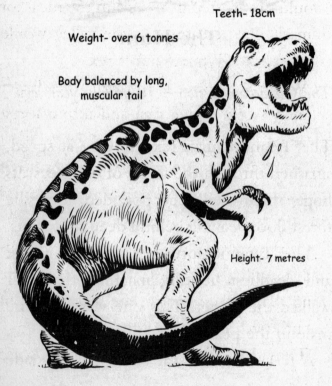

TYRANNOSAURUS REX

Teeth- 18cm

Weight- over 6 tonnes

Body balanced by long, muscular tail

Height- 7 metres

Somewhere up ahead he could smell blood. He began to run faster.

White Scar often used his dangerous pace to chase and catch his own prey, but he also loved to scavenge for food. If a smaller hunter brought down a kill, White Scar would simply step in and claim the meat for himself. Few creatures in the valley would argue with a Tyrannosaurus rex.

White Scar burst through the lower branches of a maple tree and into a forest clearing.

At the far end of the clearing, a group of five velociraptors were gathered around their prey.

The creatures were mean and vicious killers. Their deadliest weapon was the long sickle-like claw on the second toe of each hind foot.

They worked in packs and were

surprisingly intelligent and skilful hunters. Unlike most dinosaur hunters, they had large and useful hands that could grab and catch their prey.

VELOCIRAPTOR

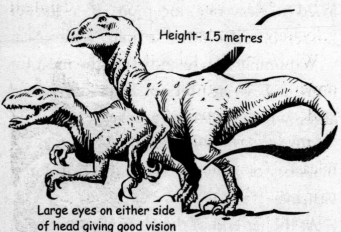

Height- 1.5 metres

Large eyes on either side of head giving good vision

Velociraptors would eat anything.

White Scar knew that he had to scare them away quickly, before they decided to make a fight of it.

The largest velociraptor opened his mouth and hissed a battle challenge. The other four stopped eating. They carefully focused their beady eyes on the advancing tyrannosaurus.

Two of them quickly moved either side of White Scar. He heard them moving into their positions and didn't look round. White Scar knew it was a standard velociraptor battle tactic.

White Scar looked down at the group leader. He opened his mighty jaws and released a deafening roar. Thick saliva splattered on to the velociraptor's face.

The velociraptor leader quickly looked either side of White Scar. Then he hissed another battle cry, this one much shorter than the first.

White Scar was an experienced fighter and knew exactly what to expect next. The second cry was supposed to distract him while the two creatures on either side of him made their move.

White Scar stepped forward half a pace and raised his powerful tail. In one smooth, unbroken movement it swung left then right.

The first velociraptor was hit on the chest and sent flying into the forest. The second attacker was caught in mid-leap. Its right forearm shattered with the impact.

White Scar leapt forward and
bellowed a roar of triumph in the
group leader's face. Having seen his
troops beaten, their leader decided against
an all-out fight. Survival was more
important than victory. Anyway, most of
the spoils had already been eaten.

The group followed their leader's retreat
and disappeared into the forest, with its
two injured members limping behind.

White Scar let out another triumphant
roar and stepped forward to claim his prize.

The velociraptors had only been feeding for a few minutes but they had already reduced their prey to little more than just bones.

White Scar's jaws opened wide and he swallowed down the remaining meat in one quick gulp.

Turning his bulky form, he made his way back into the trees. He was moving more slowly now. A gentle rippling of green branches betrayed his passage through the forest.

He wanted food and he wanted it soon. He could feel the blood-lust rising inside him.

He headed south towards the rich green lands of the valley floor. It was here that the forest met the grazing lands, where herds of plant-eaters would be feeding. This was his best hope of making a certain killing.

With surprising grace for a creature of his

size and strength, White Scar made his way towards the very edge of the thick forest.

On the grassy plain beyond, a herd of plant-eating torosaurus was feeding in the noon sun. Hidden within the forest's dark shadows White Scar could wait and choose his kill carefully.

As he moved closer, he caught sight of something moving just beyond the forest's edge. It was a young torosaurus. Barely a year old, its horns were not yet fully grown.

It had wandered away from its parents, attracted by the deep green leaves of the forest trees.

Perfect.

White Scar moved in for the kill.

The young torosaurus continued to take giant mouthfuls of leaves from an oak tree.

White Scar stepped closer, always careful to stay in the shadows where he could not be seen. Huge, sticky drops of saliva dripped from his massive red tongue.

As White Scar stepped forward
a shape suddenly flashed by him,
appearing from the undergrowth.

It was an oviraptor. The arrival of White
Scar had disturbed the ugly creature from
its resting place.

The fleeing oviraptor ran past the
torosaurus. The young animal looked up,
and found itself staring straight into the
eyes of White Scar.

For a second it seemed frozen to the spot
with fear. White Scar threw himself

towards his prey, his jaws open wide.

The youngster broke into a gallop, heading back towards the main body of the herd.

White Scar lunged and caught the right-hand side of the young torosaurus' body. But it was just a glancing blow and not enough to stop the animal racing back to its parents.

Alerted by the noise and his offspring's cries of pain, an adult torosaurus ran quickly towards White Scar.

A fully grown adult torosaurus could be a match even for a Tyrannosaurus rex. But White Scar was frantic with hunger and he could not stop himself now.

The adult torosaurus and White Scar stood facing each other. The plant-eater pawed the ground, getting ready to attack.

White Star let out a long, threatening roar.

The torosaurus lowered its head,

and with its massive horns angled to the front, it began its charge.

As the beast hurtled towards him, White Scar waited until the last moment, then raised his leg. He brought his three-toed foot down on the torosaurus' head, carefully avoiding contact with the horns.

White Scar tried to pin his enemy down. However, throwing his body weight first in one direction and then the other, the torosaurus quickly broke free.

White Scar moved away, waiting for the next charge. It came quickly, but this time he simply side-stepped it.

On the third charge, the torosaurus's horn went smashing into White Scar's lower leg. The great hunter gave out a roar of pain.

The torosaurus stepped back and prepared to plunge his horn in again.

The step back was a mistake.

In a split second, White Scar raised his uninjured leg and brought it down hard on top of the torosaurus' skull. The creature's front legs gave way and he crashed to the ground, pinned underneath the meat-eater's weight.

White Scar opened his jaws and leant down for the kill.

As his teeth were closing in on the torosaurus' back, White Scar suddenly felt searing pain shoot up his other leg.

He looked down to see that the young torosaurus had returned to enter the battle. It had run its small horn through the back of the hunter's leg.

White Scar lost his footing and was forced to release the adult from his grip. Immediately, the torosaurus thrust its horns into White Scar's exposed and unprotected belly.

It was a fatal wound. White Scar's body hit the ground before he even realized he was dying.

The adult torosaurus pushed the youngster back towards the herd once more. The herd had lost none of its members and could now graze in safety again.

A peaceful silence descended on the area. The body of a tyrannosaurus was of no interest to a herd of plant-eaters. To others, though, it was a different story.

Slowly and carefully the creatures left the safety of the forest and headed towards the motionless body.

The creatures were mean and vicious killers. Their deadliest weapon was the long sickle-like claw on the second toe of each hind foot.

They worked in packs and were surprisingly intelligent and skilful hunters. Unlike most dinosaur hunters, they had large and useful hands that could grab and catch their prey.

Velociraptors would eat anything.

Did you know...?

Dinosaur hunters

1. Dinosaurs totally dominated the Earth for 165 million years – making them the most successful animals of all time as well as being the largest animals ever to walk on Earth. Most terrifying of all the dinosaurs was the biggest and most powerful meat-eater, Tyrannosaurus rex, a name which means "tyrant lizard".

2. A fully-grown T. rex weighed 5–6 tonnes (as much as an elephant) and had such a big appetite that it ate its own weight in fresh meat every week. It probably hunted herds of duckbilled and

horned dinosaurs, and it could move at speeds of up to 20 miles per hour.

3. Tyrannosaurus rex comes from a family of dinosaurs called tyrannosaurids, who lived between 136 and 65 million years ago. They all had huge heads and bodies, with massive teeth, and powerful back legs. Their arms were small and weak compared to the rest of their bodies.

4. In 1990, the world's largest T. rex was found in South Dakota, USA. It is the most complete T. rex ever discovered, with 85 to 90% of its bones preserved, and it goes by the unlikely name of Sue!

5. The first fossil remains of *Tyrannosaurus*

rex were discovered by the famous fossil-hunter Barnum Brown in Hell Creek, Montana, USA in 1902. Since then other T. rexes have been found in many countries around the world.

6. No one knows for certain how long dinosaurs lived, but scientists think that a tyrannosaurus probably had a life span of about a hundred years.

The Search

The Cretaceous period

The female protoceratops watched the approaching storm with unease. Underneath her body were 30 precious eggs hidden in a circular nest. Some of the eggs belonged to her and some to the other females in the herd.

It was her turn to stand guard over the nest, but the dark twisting shape on the horizon was worrying her. The wind was getting worse. She knew a bad sand-storm was on the way and soon she would have to leave the nest and look for shelter.

Hiding behind a nearby ridge in the rocks was a small oviraptor. The animal was an egg-stealer, who survived by raiding the nests of other dinosaurs and stealing their eggs.

This oviraptor was waiting for a chance to sneak into the protoceratops' nest. Its powerful beak would then break open the eggs so it could feed.

At last the adult protoceratops moved away

from the nest looking for shelter. This was the oviraptor's chance.

The oviraptor felt the harsh wind pick up. The storm was very close now, but the little creature was hungry and decided the raid was worth the risk. As the creature moved nearer the nest, the full force of the sand-storm hit the oviraptor's body. . .

65 million years later...

When Roy Chapman Andrews arrived back in the Gobi Desert in April 1922, he felt like he had finally come home. He climbed to the top of the highest sand dune he could see and looked out over the

bright reds and dry yellows of the desert
landscape.

In their continuing quest for new
dinosaur finds, scientists often have to travel
all over the world. Important fossils have
been found everywhere from the steamy
Amazon jungle to the snowy wastes of the
South Pole.

 To get the job done, the
dinosaur scientists often have to be
part explorer and part adventurer as

well. Roy Chapman Andrews was both. With his wide-brimmed hat, long rifle, and love of exploring he was in many ways the original Indiana Jones.

He had visited the Gobi Desert once before and had decided that it would make the perfect place for a major fossil-hunting expedition.

The Gobi Desert is a huge and dangerous area of barren sand that stretches across parts of Mongolia and China. This vast wasteland is over 1,600 km wide and 800 km across.

Travellers faced not just high temperatures and scorching sun, but also roaming bands of hostile bandits known to rob and murder. To add to the desert's charm, the local wildlife included many poisonous snakes and scorpions.

Andrews had persuaded the American Museum of Natural History to let him launch the expedition. No one had ever discovered dinosaur fossils in central Asia before and Andrews wanted to be the first.

He had organized a team of experts to take with him who could examine the fossils as they found them. For his second-in-command, Andrews had chosen Walter Granger. He was a dinosaur scientist who, Andrews knew, was used to working in very difficult and dangerous conditions.

Knowing the many problems of desert travel, Andrews wisely decided on a fleet of cars and trucks so they could cover more ground. Their food and petrol would follow behind on a team of 125 camels.

Andrews transported a staggering 18 tonnes of equipment from New York to the edge of the desert.

Although the Museum believed in him, Andrews had many critics back in America. People who said that the whole expedition was a waste of both time and money and that they would find nothing worthwhile. If he didn't make some important finds, then the president of the Museum who approved the trip might well be sacked. Andrews knew the pressure was on to get results.

The expedition headed east into the desert. They stopped regularly to examine the rocks around them but for the first week there was no sign of any fossils. But Andrews was patient.

He had taken great care to plan every last detail of the expedition. He knew that the local people would be very suspicious of strangers from another country.

The first night that Andrews pitched the expedition's tents his companions saw that they were all made of a dark blue material that was decorated with dozens of yellow bats.

When the local tribesmen saw them, they nodded in approval.

"They seem happy," noted Walter

Granger, a little puzzled.

Andrews pointed towards the tents and smiled. "These are traditional Mongol tents," he explained quietly. "To these people, yellow bats are a sign of good fortune."

"Let's hope they are for us as well," said Granger, turning in for the night. After the long day's journey, everyone was looking forward to some much-needed rest. But they didn't sleep for long.

About four in the morning, the explorers were woken up by the sound of an approaching storm. A great cloud of swirling red dust was heading straight for their camp.

"Sandstorm!" yelled Andrews. "Lay face down in the sand! Cover your eyes!"

Seeing the sandstorm moving quickly towards them, Granger decided he would be better off back inside his tent. The wind got stronger and stronger, throwing sand and gravel at the outside of the tent until suddenly it began blasting sand through the walls.

To Granger's horror, he heard a sudden rip of cloth as his tent was torn in half by the wind. Sand blasted him from every angle and he threw himself down on the ground.

The only thing to do was to cover his eyes and wait for it to pass. The ground was the safest place to be – Andrews had been right. Granger had learnt a useful lesson.

Andrews and his men continued their search for fossils, but the only things they found among the desert rock were large numbers of deadly brown pit vipers. It was not unusual for each man to disturb ten or more of the poisonous snakes during an average day's work.

Andrews became friendly with
a local group of Mongol
tribesmen. They began to trust him
and one day they gave him some very
exciting information. They told him about
a special place where there were old bones
"as big as a man's body".

Andrews ordered the expedition to head
straight for the area they suggested, a place
called Iren Dabasu. They arrived late in the
day and decided to make camp for the
night, and explore tomorrow.

Andrews began setting up his tent and
started to bang the main stake into the
ground. He hit it with a hammer, but the
pole wouldn't break the surface of the
earth. When Andrews looked down he saw
why. Sitting on the top of the sand was a
huge dinosaur bone!

He began to look around and quickly
realized that there were bones and

fragments of bones everywhere around them.

"Over here!"

Andrews called to the rest of his men who came running from all over their new camp-site. He got down on his hands and knees and began brushing away the sand from around the fossil bone so they could take a better look. There was no mistake.

"We have just found," said Andrews to his men, "the first dinosaur fossil ever discovered in central Asia."

They had done it!

Andrews and his team set about their work. Among their finds were the fossil bones of new dinosaurs, including one particularly important skull.

The skull was sent back to New York where the Museum's experts realized it came from the animal that was the forerunner of  triceratops – the famous horned dinosaur. The new discovery was named "Protoceratops andrewsi" in honour of Andrews himself.

But the expedition's most important finds were yet to come.

At the time of Andrews' expedition no one knew how dinosaurs had babies. Many people thought that the dinosaurs must have laid eggs, but no one knew for sure.

Andrews' expedition was about to solve one of the biggest dinosaur mysteries of all.

One hot afternoon one of Andrews' fellow scientists, George Olsen, called him over to look at a new find. First of all, Andrews thought he was looking at a piece of broken skull-bone.

Then Olsen said, "Look at these, still in the rock."

Andrews' eyes followed Olsen's finger as he pointed at a number of oval objects on the ground ahead. They looked for all the world like they were enormous eggs. Each one was 15 cm long.

Andrews could not believe his eyes. No one before them had ever found anything like this.

"These must be dinosaur eggs," he said, holding one carefully in his hand. "They simply can't be anything else."

By the end of the day, the team had found an amazing 17 eggs. They had unearthed a nesting area where millions of years ago adult protoceratops had come to breed and watch their young hatch.

On top of their other discoveries, they had now made dinosaur history.

 The next day's find was even stranger.

"Come and look at this," said

Granger, the following morning.

Andrews looked down at the piece of sandstone that Granger had been carefully excavating.

It was another cluster of protoceratops eggs, but on top of them was something very unusual.

"Look, it's the skeleton of a small meat-eater with a large beak. My guess is that it was trying to steal some of the eggs when a sudden sandstorm killed it," said Granger, thinking back to his own sandstorm experience.

The scientists back in New York agreed and named the little dinosaur "Oviraptor" – a name which means "egg thief".

Andrews returned to New York a hero. His expedition had been a huge success. His dinosaur eggs made news around the world and photographers offered thousands of dollars just to be allowed to take pictures of the eggs. Thousands of people flocked to the Museum to see them.

Andrews' bravery and vision inspired a whole generation of dinosaur lovers who grew up wanting to follow in his footsteps.

The fossils discovered by his expedition opened a window allowing scientists a look back into the Earth's distant past. For the first time, they allowed humans to understand the daily struggle for survival of creatures that vanished from the world millions of years ago.

Did you know...?

Dinosaur science

1. Scientists who study dinosaurs are called paleontologists, and their study is split into many different areas. For example, a "paleoscatologist" is a scientist who spends their entire time studying fossilized dinosaur droppings!

2. Scientists have found out that most dinosaur bones have growth rings, which show how old the dinosaur was when it died – like the growth rings on the trunk of a tree. These have shown that small dinosaurs probably had shorter lives than big ones.

3. It's not just fossil bones that give scientists information. Fossilized trackways are important as well. A dinosaur's footprints can show how dinosaurs moved around, how fast they could run, and their hunting behaviour.

4. No one knows what colours dinosaurs really were when they were alive because skin never becomes fossilized. Dinosaurs could have been green and brown so they could hide among the trees easily, or bright colours like some modern birds and lizards.

5. Scientists love giving dinosaurs long names. The longest single dinosaur name ever belongs to a plant-eating dinosaur called "Micropachycephalosaurus"!

6. Not all dinosaurs were huge beasts – in the late 1850s, a meat-eating dinosaur about the size of a chicken was discovered, and named "Compsognathus".

Escape

The Cretaceous period

The herd of triceratops was grazing peacefully on the valley slopes. Its green sides rose gently above them, reaching up to the volcano and its steaming lava pit at the very top of the valley. A fast-flowing river ran along the centre of the valley, tumbling its way towards the sea.

The sound of far-away thunder rumbled in from the distance. Dark Bone, an adult male, stopped feeding and moved closer to his mate and their hatchling. Fast-moving clouds were blowing in from the nearby coast.

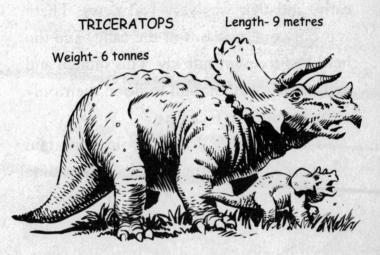

TRICERATOPS Length- 9 metres

Weight- 6 tonnes

The herd had had a good season and many new hatchlings had been born. Most of the youngsters were now ready for the long walk south to fresh grazing lands.

A thunderclap suddenly exploded overhead. The younger animals pressed against their parents for protection. Dark Bone watched as black storm-clouds appeared over the horizon.

This year's rainy season was about to start early, and that was very bad news. There was only one way out of the valley and the herd had to use it quickly. This sudden and early storm was enough to flood their only escape route.

In an instant a hail of cold hard rain blasted down from the sky. It was time to leave. As if an unspoken call had gone out, the

herd prepared to move off.

From overhead, a dark shape struggled against the powerful winds and swooped low over the herd. It was a pteranodon fighting to get back to its nest before the storm got any worse.

The huge creature rose quickly on an up-draught of air, then, with one graceful movement, it disappeared over the side of the hill.

Further up the valley, the grey clouds had now reached the volcano's peak. Rain fell into the pit of red-hot lava, making huge clouds of hissing steam. Above the volcano, streaks of purple lightning flashed through the sky.

The herd began to move down the valley slope, one animal following another. Dark Bone and his mate moved along, carefully keeping their baby in between them.

Just in front of Dark Bone was Broken Horn. One of his horns had been snapped in a battle now long forgotten. Years ago, he had led the walk out of the valley. Now he was no longer a leader, just one of the many older members of the herd. He gave a snort and shuffled forward with the rest.

The river that ran through the centre of

the valley began to swell with the rain-water flooding down from the higher slopes. It was now a race against time. The river was rising with each passing moment.

From the distance came a sudden, heart-stopping sound. It was the call of an albertosaurus – a huge meat-eater. Whenever the herd moved, there were always hunters waiting to feed.

Broken Horn was getting more and more tired with each step and Dark Bone nudged the older male's rear to keep him moving.

At the front of the herd, the leaders came to a sudden halt. They had reached the point where a stream flowed into the main river. Normally it was just a few centimetres deep. Now the rain had swollen it into a dangerous rush of water.

There was no choice but to cross it. To stay in the valley was certain death. The two males at the front splashed into the water and fought the powerful current as they waded across. Even for them, it wasn't easy. One by one, the herd plunged in and struggled to the other side. When it was his turn, Broken Horn dived straight in.

Already frightened by the storm, Dark Bone's hatchling froze with fear. Dark Bone pushed him into the water, then waded in himself. The father and his mate kept the youngster in between them so that he was always protected from the powerful current.

They were nearly across when disaster struck.

Broken Horn was tiring fast and a rush of water made him suddenly lose his footing. He crashed into Dark Bone who fell sideways.

Without his father to protect him, the small hatchling had to fight against the water on his own. He had time to let out a short squeal of panic, then he disappeared. A wall of foaming white water swept him away and in a second he was out of sight.

Dark Bone's mate let out a terrible cry of anguish.

The parents and Broken Horn scrambled out of the water. They had survived the crossing, but the precious hatchling – their first – was gone.

The centre of the storm was directly above them now and violet lightning leapt from cloud to cloud. High in the valley, the lightning struck a group of pine trees on the river's edge. The trees crashed into the river, and floated a short distance until they were caught on a narrow bend. They made a temporary dam, blocking the flow of the river. Upstream, the water level grew higher and higher.

The herd had reached the lower slopes where the river widened out. A little further and they would be able to use the pass to leave the valley and climb into the hills again heading south.

Dark Bone and his mate followed Broken Horn along the slippery track near the curve of the river. As they walked, Dark Bone's mate suddenly threw her head to one side, listening carefully. Dark Bone did the same, but could only hear the footsteps of the animals around him. Then Dark Bone heard it too.

A faint cry.

In the shallows of the river was a familiar shape – their hatchling! He had been washed downriver and had been caught in the reeds near the water's edge. He was weak and tired, but he was alive.

Upstream, the dam made by the fallen trees was about to burst. When it did, a flash-flood of terrifying force would gush down the valley.

The hatchling needed to get out of the water quickly, but was too tired to climb the steep riverbank without help. Dark

Bone dived in and started to push the hatchling towards safety.

He was making good progress when he was interrupted by a loud and hungry roar. An albertosaurus was wading through the river towards them with its eyes fixed greedily on the helpless hatchling.

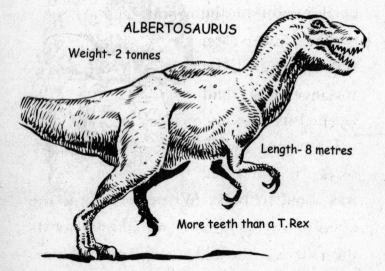

ALBERTOSAURUS

Weight- 2 tonnes

Length- 8 metres

More teeth than a T.Rex

Dark Bone pushed the hatchling towards the bank with all his strength.

The albertosaurus continued wading through the rushing river, its jaws open wide. Though Dark Bone was nearly exhausted, he turned round ready for a battle. He knew that it was a fight he would lose.

The albertosaurus was so close that Dark Bone could smell the pieces of rotting flesh stuck between its enormous teeth.

The meat-eater was within striking distance now and opened its jaws once more, ready to take its first bite.

Suddenly a bulky form splashed into the water between Dark Bone and the meat-eater. It was the old male, Broken Horn. Most of the herd had passed by now, but Broken Horn had hung back to help any lost members.

Now faced with two enemies, the albertosaurus had to decide what to do next. The delay gave Dark Bone just enough time to shove the hatchling on to the bank. Dark Bone's mate was waiting to help the tired youngster away from danger.

Upstream, the dam finally burst and a wall of water rushed down the valley blasting everything in its path.

In the lower part of the river, the albertosaurus saw its meal escaping and roared with rage. It edged forward, still undecided which triceratops to attack first.

The albertosaurus turned its head to look upriver. A terrible rumbling noise was coming from up the valley: it was deeper than thunder. The sound was heavy and low like an earthquake. At that moment the water itself seemed to shudder.

When the albertosaurus looked back, it saw that the two triceratops had already scrambled up the riverbank. No matter. They were tired. The albertosaurus was strong and hungry. It stepped towards the bank and opened its jaws to let out a roar of anger.

Before it could make a sound, though, a huge wall of water crashed into it. The impact of the water broke several of its bones. A moment later, the water washed its body out of sight.

The flash-flood spilled over the river bank, but Dark Bone's mate sheltered their hatchling. They waited until the great rush of water had passed. Then the group of four triceratops made their way out of the valley and joined the rest of the herd.

They had survived another escape from the valley and ahead of them waited fresh green feeding grounds. Dark Bone gently pushed the hatchling forward and together they took the first step on the long journey south.

Did you know...?

The dinosaur world

1. When the very first dinosaurs walked the Earth, the planet was very different from how it is today. All the land was stuck together in one huge lump called Pangaea, surrounded by a single sea.

2. While dinosaurs ruled the land, enormous reptiles swam in the oceans. Among them were plesiosaurs, sea–living creatures with long necks and large flippers who lived on fish.

3. Although plesiosaurs lived in the oceans, they breathed air. Some plesiosaur

fossils have been found with small stones in their stomachs, which may mean that they swallowed stones to help them grind up their food.

4. At the time of the dinosaurs, flying reptiles called pterosaurs were the masters of the sky. They were closely related to the dinosaurs, and the largest one so far discovered was in Texas, USA, and had a wingspan of 15 metres across – the size of a small aircraft!

5. Crocodiles shared the Earth with the dinosaurs and are still around today. Dinosaur-age crocodiles, however, were much bigger than the modern kind. One, called "Deinosuchus", was 15 metres long!

That's big enough to take a bite out of even a T. rex!

6. There were far fewer types of plants and animals in the dinosaurs' world than we have in ours today. The most common plants were ever-green conifer trees, which were the most important food for plant-eating dinosaurs.

The Boy Who Loved Dinosaurs

Montana, America. 47 years ago

The boy who loved dinosaurs climbed over the top of a tall ridge and looked down. Below him the other side of the ridge dropped two metres very steeply.

In the ridge wall the boy could see different-coloured levels of rock just like the layers in a cake. His heart jumped. This was just what they were looking for.

"Dad! Over here!"

A man wearing mountain boots climbed the ridge in great strides. "What have you found, Jack?"

"An exposed cliff face, just like the book said, Dad."

The man stepped over the edge of the steep wall and slid down, using the huge heels on his boots to act as brakes. Then he turned and saw the boy was making his own way down without waiting for instructions.

"Careful, Jack. Wait till I'm ready to..."

"I can do it. Stop worrying," said the boy, sliding down on his backside in a great cloud of dust.

Father and son began to examine the rock wall. Some layers were dry and crumbled easily, others were hard and sharp.

"There!" said the boy. He pointed to a curved white shape in the rock that was barely visible. It was long, maybe half a metre – perhaps a leg bone. In his mind, the boy imagined the bone covered with dinosaur flesh. What colour would it be? Green? Brown?

The boy imagined the leg moving. He saw the huge creature running – perhaps sprinting away from danger. More than anything in the world, the boy wanted to take the fossil home and make it part of his collection.

His father handed him the hammer and chisel. The boy positioned the chisel against the rock face and prepared to swing the hammer.

"Careful," said the man.

"I know. I do know how to do this," said the boy.

A second later, and he brought the hammer swinging down...

25 years later...

Disappointment showed on every line on Jack Horner's face as he finished searching another barren canyon. They had been hunting duckbill dinosaurs for three weeks now and had found nothing. The summer of 1978 was nearly over.

He walked back towards his car and saw that his companion, Bob Makela was already waiting for him. As he got closer to the car, Jack shook his head sadly.

"Nothing in the other valley either," said Bob, and they silently climbed inside the vehicle.

"I really thought we had a good chance

there," said Jack. He started the engine and they drove away, the wheels of their car kicking up a spray of fine yellow dust.

"We've got time to visit one more site before the end of the vacation," said Bob, getting out the road maps to look up the route.

Jack Horner and his friend Bob Makela had spent their summer holiday searching for fossils of baby dinosaurs in Montana, USA.

Jack had begun collecting fossils when he was seven and had desperately wanted to become a top dinosaur scientist. However, Jack had a reading disability called dyslexia, which made it very difficult for him to read and write. He was smart all right, but just not good at putting it down on paper.

Thanks to his dyslexia, Jack had failed his degree course. He had finally got a job working with fossils, but it was limited to getting them ready to be looked at by the proper scientists.

Jack dreamed of making a discovery of his own that would make the real scientists finally notice him.

He had become interested in the fossils of baby dinosaurs after he had found a dinosaur egg in western Montana the year before.

Dinosaur eggs were rare, but the remains of baby dinosaur were ever rarer. In fact, no one had ever found fossils of baby dinosaurs in America or Europe. The only dinosaur nests known anywhere in the world were the ones discovered by Roy Chapman Andrews' expedition to the Gobi Desert in 1921, over 50 years before.

Jack wondered why fossils of baby dinosaurs had never been found. It was one of dinosaur science's biggest mysteries.

There were many fossil beds of duckbill dinosaurs in Jack's home state of Montana. Duckbills usually lived on the land near the sea or near rivers. Jack wondered if perhaps they always went somewhere else to breed. Some animals in the world today move hundreds of miles to have their young. What if some dinosaurs did the same? What if the proper scientists were looking in the wrong places?

When Jack explained his ideas to some of the scientists where he worked they told him he was wasting his time. Now it looked as if he'd done just that.

 "Your idea could still be right," said Bob, quietly, as they drove along the highway.

Jack just grunted. He was in no mood

to talk at the moment. The museum where he worked didn't pay him to look for fossils and once his holiday time was over in a few days' time, that would be his chance gone for another year.

When they got back to their hotel in the little town where they were staying, there was an unusual message waiting for them.

"It's from the people that run the rock shop up on West Street," said the hotel manager.

"They heard that there was a couple of dinosaur experts staying in town and they wondered if you'd go take a look at something for them. They think they've got a rib bone or something."

The two friends agreed to stop by the shop the next morning on their way out of town. They were exhausted after spending the day searching the hot desert for fossils. It was all the more tiring when they kept coming back empty-handed.

"Maybe it'll be something interesting," said Bob, as they pulled up outside the rock shop the next day. Jack smiled at his friend: Bob was always the optimist.

The shop was a dusty Aladdin's cave, stacked with rocks, crystals and fossils, all of which were for sale. The owners, Marian and John Brandvold, greeted them and then produced their mystery bone from behind the counter.

Jack's heart sank the second he saw it. It was just a piece of fossilized tree branch. Sure, it was shaped like a bone, but that was just coincidence. He had to explain just that to the disappointed shop-owners.

While they were in the shop the pair had a look round at the items on sale. There was the usual selection of common fossils designed to appeal to tourists.

On one of the shelves behind the counter was a rusty coffee tin filled with small fossils. Jack picked it up and noticed two dusty pieces of grey bone sitting at the top of the tin.

He recognized what they were straight away. One was the leg bone of a duckbill dinosaur and the other was part of its jawbone. In an adult duckbill the leg bone would have been over a metre in length – but these were just a few centimetres long! There was no doubt about it. These bones were from baby duckbills! But where had they come from?

"I can tell you exactly, I'll show you on a map," volunteered John Brandvold. "We found them here, on a ranch near the town of Choteau." Jack knew the area well – he had hunted for fossils around there when he was a child.

Outside, Jack made an emergency call to his university to ask for more time off to follow up the clues he had found. They immediately agreed and sent him 500 dollars expenses.

The two friends drove to where the baby dinosaur bones had been found. Were they a fluke or would there be others?

The baby bones had been found in what the shop owners called a "hump on the ground" in the middle of a cattle ranch. The bump was two metres across and one metre high.

The two men got permission from the owners and then started digging. One of the locals in town had heard what was happening and had called a television station. Soon there were several camera crews watching the men work – waiting for their first results.

Jack and Bob usually used a garden hose and a piece of netting to examine the first spadefuls of earth. Jack would carefully break the earth into small pieces, then Bob would use the spray of the hose to break it down further. The soil would be washed away, but any small stones, fossils or bones would be caught in the netting and be saved.

"Ready?" asked Jack.

"Let's do it!" replied Bob.

It was time to find out if this trip was just another waste of time as well.

Bob turned on the hose and began the difficult process of washing away the mud and earth. It was especially difficult with a TV camera watching your every move.

As the mud was washed away, Jack and Bob saw bone after bone getting caught on the netting. It soon became clear that they had hit the jackpot. In a few short hours they recovered the bones of 15 baby duckbills from that one hollow alone! Nobody had found anything like this before – it was beyond their wildest dreams.

The baby duckbills would each have stood about one metre high. Their jawbones revealed that although they  were only young they had already worn down their teeth. This started Jack thinking.

Until this discovery, dinosaurs were not thought to have ever taken care of their babies. Scientists knew that dinosaurs laid eggs, but thought that they then abandoned them.

Jack pieced together the clues that he had found just as Sherlock Holmes would have done.

"Look at this, Bob. At the bottom of the nest are the remains of the dinosaurs' eggs. But the shells are completely crushed, so the young must have been in the nest for a long while, right?"

"Makes sense," agreed Bob.

"But look at the jawbones. The young had worn teeth which meant they were eating solid food and we know they must have been a few months old before they left the nest. Yeah?"

"So?" asked Bob.

"So if the babies were eating solid food then something had to be feeding them – and that something had to be their parents."

"You've just proved dinosaurs looked after their young!" said Bob, amazed.

If duckbills took care of their young, then it was very likely that other dinosaurs did as well. It was the first time that anyone had been able to say for sure that dinosaurs looked after their young like that.

Jack and Bob named the new type of duckbill they had found "Maiasaurus" which means "good mother lizard".

Jack Horner put his ideas into a scientific paper and very quickly scientists everywhere agreed with him. Suddenly the young man who had failed his degree had scientists everywhere listening to him.

In the years afterwards, Jack Horner went on to become one of the most respected dinosaur scientists in the world. He was even hired to be the dinosaur expert for the *Jurassic Park* films and advised the movie-makers on how the real animals would have behaved.

The boy who had fallen in love with dinosaurs when he was seven had changed dinosaur science for ever.

Did you know...?

Dinosaur behaviour

1. Most dinosaurs laid eggs with hard shells, like modern birds and reptiles. The eggs were often laid in mud nests, and covered over with leaves. Some types of dinosaur would go back to the same place every year to lay their eggs.

2. Although the duckbilled dinosaurs fed and looked after their young in nests, a lot of young dinosaurs had to fend for themselves, and very many of them were killed before they grew up.

3. We know that a lot of dinosaurs lived in

big herds or packs, thanks to large groups of fossils found in the same place. Many plant-eaters moved in herds to protect themselves. Some meat-eaters hunted in packs so they could attack and kill plant-eaters much bigger in size than themselves.

4. Dinosaurs usually walked on their toes, using their tails for balance. How fast they moved depended on their shape and size — huge dinosaurs with short legs, like "Diplodocus" moved very slowly, while some bird-like dinosaurs could probably run at up to 40 miles per hour.

5. Although some people still think of dinosaurs as slow and stupid creatures, their actual brain power varied a great deal.

Stegosaurus had one of the smallest brains for a big dinosaur, while others had the brain-power of modern birds.

First Kill

The Late Jurassic period, 145 million years ago

The allosaurus leader scanned the horizon for any sign of life. The three other allosaurus following him did the same, but, however hard they looked, they couldn't see anything moving. The rocky desert around them offered little chance of finding food.

The leader sniffed the air. From somewhere upwind the scents of a forest drifted towards them on the breeze. The four creatures moved on, following the scents, their massive feet leaving huge markings behind in the sand.

Until recently the four male allosaurus had been part of a much larger herd. As they grew older, however, they had been driven out of the herd and left to fend for themselves. Now it was time for the young hunters to form their own pack.

They were still learning the art of hunting and so far they had had few successes.

After they had left the main pack, the four animals had set out across an area of rocky desert. They needed to find their own territory — an area where they could live and hunt that would belong to just them. They had been moving for days without any rest and were now exhausted and very hungry.

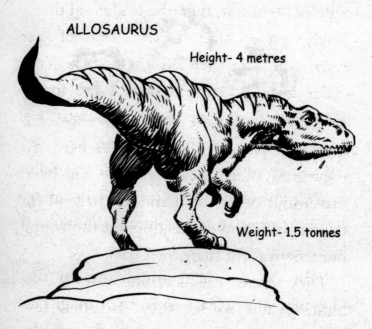

ALLOSAURUS

Height- 4 metres

Weight- 1.5 tonnes

They struggled up the side of a steep ridge. As they reached the top, their eyes caught sight of the distant green of a forest.

The tall pine trees rippled gently in the midday breeze. Wherever there were plants, there would be plant-eaters – in other words, food.

The allosaurus moved quickly to the edge of the forest, then the leader led them slowly inside. After the dry heat of the desert, the forest felt cool and dark. The leader leant down and sniffed the forest floor. One fresh scent-trail stood out from the rest and he breathed it in greedily.

They set off following the trail, carefully stalking through the thick undergrowth. The tall fir trees cast a shadowy gloom over everything.

Soon the four allosaurus came to the edge of a small clearing. In the sunlight at the centre was a stegosaurus, noisily munching fern leaves. Its mouth darted between different plants, picking off the fresh green shoots from each of them. The cheek pouches on the side of its mouth were full of half-chewed food.

Along its back was a row of large bony plates shaped like triangles. This stegosaurus was an old male and one of its back plates had a bite-sized piece missing from its corner. At the end of its tail were four razor-sharp spikes – a deadly weapon.

Eager for their first kill, the allosaurus leader and the others stepped into the clearing. Startled by the noise, the stegosaurus looked around, his tail flicking into life.

The second allosaurus rushed forward and there was a sickening thud as one of the stegosaurus' tail spikes imbedded in his leg.

The direct hit had been more luck than good judgement, but the effect was just the same. The allosaurus let out a roar of pain. The deadly tail flicked into life again, rising up and hitting the young allosaurus full in the stomach. The animal fell to the ground, dying.

The stegosaurus now saw that his attackers were young, not yet fully grown. He turned his head and went back to feeding.

The allosaurus leader stepped forward, determined to sink his teeth into the plant-eater's neck for revenge. But as the leader moved into range, the stegosaurus' tail swung into life again.

Although he appeared to be ignoring

them, the older beast had positioned himself at the perfect angle to land another powerful blow. His tail swung quickly through the air, but the allosaurus leader realized what was happening just in time. The spikes missed him by just a few centimetres.

The stegosaurus took another mouthful of leaves, as if to prove a point, then wandered away into the dark of the forest.

Their attack had been a complete failure. The allosaurus were still hungry and worse, now one of their number was dead. The pack had been reduced from four to three. They could not afford to lose another member or they would themselves be in danger of becoming a meal for a larger meat-eater.

Left with empty stomachs, the three animals set off into the heart of the forest. Smaller dinosaurs darted away between the trees when they heard the pack approach. They were careful to stay out of sight of the unwelcome intruders.

Eventually the trees began to thin out and the forest opened on to a rich green meadow. A herd of brachiosaurus were feeding just beyond the trees. Their long necks curved gracefully as they picked leaves from the branches.

As the allosaurus emerged from the forest, the adult brachiosaurus watched them with suspicious eyes. The younger members of the herd were feeding together in the middle, protected by a circle of adults. The allosaurus were in no mood for another fight so soon and passed on quickly.

Beyond the herd of plant-eaters, the ground began to rise quickly, leading towards tree-covered mountains in the distance. Perhaps somewhere on the higher ground they could at last find a territory of their own.

As they walked on, the allosaurus suddenly found a huge and bulky form blocking their path. It was a fully grown female brachiosaurus. Her large wet nostrils were urgently smelling the air. Perhaps she was looking for fresh food supplies for when the herd moved on.

The allosaurus passed her carefully and continued along the track. The path started to climb sharply now. It curved its way along the edge of a rocky cliff, leading towards the distant mountains. As they walked, the sheer drop to the hard rocks below became greater and greater.

The allosaurus leader suddenly stopped dead in his tracks and listened carefully. Something was moving just ahead of them around the curve in the path.

Were they about to invade the territory of another meat-eater? Such a mistake could easily prove fatal.

The leader advanced slowly and checked around the corner. Stumbling along the cliff path, looking rather confused, was a young brachiosaurus – probably no more than a year old. He had wandered away from the main herd and got lost.

The young animal turned the corner and almost barged straight into the allosaurus pack. When he saw the three meat-eaters, he panicked.

His nostrils flared with fear and he turned and bolted back up the path. The allosaurus sprinted after him. Two of them overtook him and turned to stop his escape.

He was surrounded. Two allosaurus blocked his way up the path, while the leader blocked his escape route down.

The brachiosaurus was frozen with terror. He looked over the edge of the rocky cliff path, but there was a sheer drop of over 50 metres. He would never survive if he jumped.

The allosaurus leader let out a roar of hunger and, opening his jaws, moved forward. They would eat well today.

As the leader stepped closer to his prey, the ground suddenly shook under his feet.

He took another step and again the ground vibrated like an earthquake.

The young brachiosaurus let out a high-pitched cry. To the leader's horror, the call was answered by the adult brachiosaurus they had seen earlier. This was her hatchling.

After an unheard command from his mother, the young brachiosaurus charged past the allosaurus leader. The little animal rushed behind its mother and then headed to safety down the path.

The three allosaurus advanced towards the adult brachiosaurus, who stood her ground, giving her offspring time to escape.

Even an experienced pack of hunters would think twice before attacking a brachiosaurus. These, however, were not experienced hunters. They were beginners and all they knew was that they were hungry.

The allosaurus leader dodged under the brachiosaurus' long neck and landed a glancing blow on her thick ribcage.

The leader expected her to move back, allowing him to jump at her neck, but instead she turned sideways. Her long tail flicked across the path like a huge and powerful whip.

It smashed into the leader's chest and sent him hurtling into the cliff wall. The air was knocked out of his lungs and he collapsed into the dirt.

The brachiosaurus' tail moved menacingly across the path like a snake's tongue tasting the air. The allosaurus realized they had no chance of victory and backed away slowly.

As the forest attack had shown them earlier, death was never more than a moment away. If their shrinking pack lost another member, they would be finished as hunters.

The brachiosaurus stretched the full length of her neck towards the sky and let out another high-pitched cry. This time the noise was louder, a call of triumph.

The allosaurus attack had been another failure. Unless they found some food soon, they would begin to lose strength. No other allosaurus would join their pack if they were starving. Soon they would be hunted themselves.

The brachiosaurus turned and began to walk down the path. The allosaurus leader picked himself off the dirt floor and could do nothing but watch her depart, his belly still empty.

As the brachiosaurus reached the narrowest part of the curve in the path, there was a sudden cracking sound.

The beast's enormous weight was causing the edge of the cliff path to collapse. She struggled to keep her footing, but the more she tried to move to safety, the more the path crumbled under her.

For a split second, her huge body seemed to hang in mid-air, then she disappeared over the edge. She plummeted down, smashing on to the rocks below with a terrible sound of cracking bones.

The allosaurus moved to the edge of the path and looked over. They could hardly believe their eyes. Waiting for them on the rocks below was 80 tonnes of fresh meat. They would be able to feast for days.

The leader led the race down the cliff path towards the fallen body. He opened

his jaws wide and ripped away a huge mouthful of meat.

The pack had made their first kill.

When he had eaten his fill, the leader's roar of victory echoed down the valley. They would stay until they had picked the skeleton clean.

Over the next few days, the body would attract other allosaurus, perhaps females eager to feed. From this death would come life. Their pack would grow and they would survive to hunt again...

Did you know…?

Fossil finds

1. The ancient Chinese used to think dinosaur bones were the remains of huge dragons that lived in the sky. The bones were greatly prized and sometimes used in medicines.

2. When the Reverend Robert Plot found a large dinosaur bone in 1676, he thought that it must have come from a giant human being.

3. No one knew dinosaurs had even existed until 1822, when Ann Mantell found some giant fossil teeth and bones in

a pile of rubble that had just been dug out of the ground. Her husband, Gideon, thought the teeth must have belonged to a giant lizard that existed before humans, and he called it "Iguanadon". Iguanadons were plant-eaters that were five metres tall and 9.3 metres long.

4. In 1878, a group of coalminers in Belgium found a mass grave of iguanodons buried over 300 metres underground. Altogether over 30 skeletons were recovered from the fantastic find. They were together because the whole herd must have died at the same time in a mud-slide.

5. The biggest dinosaur yet recorded was discovered in Argentina in January 2000. It

is between 48m and 50m long, nearly as long as five double-decker buses end to end!

6. Dinosaur fossils are often sold to collectors and can fetch very high prices. A fossilized nest of ten sauropod eggs embedded in clay was recently bought for £50,000. But that's nothing compared to T. rex "Sue", who was bought by a museum in America for a staggering 8.8 million dollars!

The Dinosaur Detectives

The Lower Cretaceous period

It was late afternoon when the creature realized he was dying.

The animal moved through the lush green forest, slowing down with every step of his giant legs. He came to an area of swampland, a place where he had often hunted. Many times the creature had used his giant claws to scoop bright silver fish from its pools.

The animal waded slowly into the shallows of

the swamp. His splashes sent dozens of alarmed fish darting away to the shadows.

As the creature moved through another shallow mud pool, he stumbled and fell.

The end was close now.

He lost his footing and his huge body crashed down on to the thick brown mud. He tried to push himself up with his once-powerful forearms, but his strength was gone. He took one desperate final breath, let it out, and then stopped moving.

When the evening rain fell, water flooded into the little pool. The water level rose until mud and dirt covered the creature's body, hiding it from the eyes of hungry meat-eaters. It lay undisturbed almost for ever.

124 million years later...

The last thing I expected to do when I took my dog out for a walk was to discover a brand-new kind of dinosaur.

My name is William Walker and I've been a fossil collector for years. Every day I used to take my dog, Dodger, for a walk and I'd often choose places where I might be able to find fossils as well.

One freezing January morning in 1983, I had driven to a clay pit near the town of Dorking, south of London. It was so cold I had to rub my hands together to keep them warm. I let Dodger off his lead so he could have a run, then began to stroll around with my eyes glued firmly to the ground, searching for fossils.

 Fossils look like rocks, but they are really the remains of animals or plants that lived millions of years before mankind even existed. Fossils are rare because they are only made under certain very special conditions.

I already had a pretty big fossil collection that took up most of the spare room at home. It included fossil shells, plants, pieces of bone, and prehistoric sharks' teeth. It didn't look like I was going to add to my collection this morning. I couldn't see anything interesting as I came to the end of my walk.

I felt a bit disappointed and called to Dodger so we could go back to the car and leave. Dodger ignored me completely – he was too busy sniffing and digging at something in the rock. I walked over to where Dodger was pawing at the hard, frosty ground and leaned down. I wondered what had made him so excited.

As I looked down at what Dodger had found, I could hardly believe it. My heart

jumped as I saw that Dodger was digging at a large fossil bone. It was half-buried in the clay and Dodger was trying to dig it out.

The bone was curved like a giant claw and had a deep groove that ran along its entire length. It ended in a dangerously sharp point and would have made a deadly weapon for any dinosaur.

As I stood there looking down at the claw, I knew that I had found something very special. In all my years of fossil-hunting I had never seen anything like this.

I knelt down on my knees and very carefully began to dig out the bone. I had to use my fingers to dig through the clay around it. Then I began gently to ease it up. I had to be careful, because some fossils break very easily and I desperately wanted to get this one out of the ground in one piece.

I knew that dinosaur bones were very rare, and the bones of meat-eaters even rarer. From the size and shape of the claw, I guessed at once that it had come from a very fierce meat-eater indeed.

With the clay around it finally removed, I slowly lifted out the claw. To my great relief it came away in one piece. I wrapped my scarf round the bone to protect it.

I made a point of remembering exactly where in the clay pit I had dug up the claw, then Dodger and I headed straight back home. I spent the rest of that day and much of the night searching through all my dinosaur books. I was trying to find out what the claw might be, but I could find nothing like it in any of the books. I  didn't dare believe that this was the first time that anyone had found this kind of bone, so I kept looking.

I knew that there was only one place to take the fossil to find out about it properly – the Natural History Museum in South Kensington, London. Scientists who study dinosaur fossils are called palaeontologists. The Natural History Museum's staff included some of the best palaeontologists in the world. If they couldn't identify the claw, nobody could!

I phoned the Museum and made an appointment to take the claw in so that they could examine it. A few days later, I walked up the stone steps of the Museum's long, yellow-brick building carrying the claw still wrapped in my scarf.

I had hoped that they'd be as fascinated by it as I was — and I was right. They wanted to know everything about when, where, and how I'd found it. When it came to identifying it, though, they were at just as much of a loss as I was. But that only made it more exciting. They agreed it looked like it must have come from a large meat-eater, but they'd never seen anything like it before.

The Museum quickly decided to send a team down to the clay pit to search for any further bones still in the ground. I went down with the team and showed them exactly where to look.

I watched the team of eight people set to work. Just below the surface of the clay, they found several large fossils including the creature's long leg bone. Suddenly this was turning into one of the most important dinosaur discoveries in Britain for a hundred years!

The team leader phoned the Museum with the good news. Now it was up to them to begin the long and difficult process of getting the bones out of the ground.

The first thing they did was to make a site map. A site map records the exact position of the bones as they are in the ground. It can be very important because often the layout of the bones gives important information about how they fit together.

I visited the clay pit after work as often as I could. I saw how the scientists' excitement grew with each bone that they recovered. Lying in the same small area were the animal's skull, teeth, backbone, forearms, ribs, and back legs. Every bone they dug up made their picture of the creature a little more complete.

Some of the fossils were easy to remove

from the loose clay, while other bones were stuck to hard blocks of stone. It was very difficult work and they had to be extremely careful with every single piece of bone.

Working from dawn to dusk, it took the team three weeks of

Fore Limb

Hind Limb

0.5 m

Ribs

1m

1.5m

Skull

2m

back-breaking work to carefully remove all the fossils from the ground. To get all the bones out as safely as possible, the team also had to remove over two tonnes of rock with them!

The bones were transported back to the Natural History Museum where the real work could begin. The Museum's dinosaur detectives could now start piecing together the bones to try and find out what the animal must have looked like when it was alive.

The first thing the scientists did was to separate the bones from the rock. This involved using many different tools, from an old-fashioned hammer and chisel to a modern acid spray that melted the rock away.

Once all the bones were free of the rock, they needed to be identified and put in their correct place. This was probably the most difficult and demanding part of the whole process. It takes a scientist with many different skills to be able to put the jigsaw puzzle of mystery bones back together.

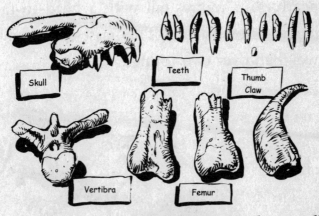

The teeth and jaws of an animal can tell you a lot about what the creature ate. This dinosaur had a long snout rather like the mouth of a crocodile – the scientists told me that they thought that our dinosaur had eaten mostly fish.

Apart from the creature's missing tail, the

Museum's team had managed to find nearly a complete skeleton. When I had first found the claw, I hadn't dreamed that there was so much more still under the clay. It was a fantastic discovery.

When it was alive, the creature had been nearly four metres tall with a head-to-tail length of ten metres. The beast would have weighed over two tonnes.

Apart from its teeth and the shape of its jaws, scientists discovered an even bigger clue as to what it used to eat. In the area where the creature's stomach would have been, they found something truly amazing. In the rock were fossilized fish scales – evidence of the creature's last meal just before its death!

With the skeleton now laid out, the Museum's scientists could say for certain that it was a type of animal that had never been found before.

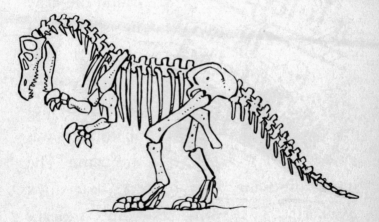

I had discovered a brand-new kind of dinosaur unknown to science. With careful detective work, the experts at the Natural

History Museum had brought the creature back to life. It was a wonderful feeling. Something that I had found had turned out to be a huge leap forward for dinosaur science.

The announcement of the dinosaur's discovery made headlines around the world. Newspapers and television people wanted to interview me about how I'd  found the claw in the first place. I was s u d d e n l y famous! Best of all though was the name. The new dinosaur was named "Baryonyx walkeri". The word "Baryonyx" means "heavy claw" because of the creature's huge claws, and "walkeri" was in honour of the man who had first found it, William

Walker. Me.

In the last 200 years, scientists have discovered and named about 400 types of dinosaur. Most scientists agree that many times that number remain unknown. Those new kinds of dinosaur are out there somewhere buried in the ground, just waiting to be discovered. It's an exciting thought, and it's why I'll never, ever, give up looking...

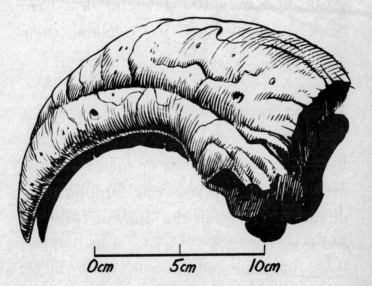

0cm   5cm   10cm

Did you know...?

The end of the dinosaurs

1. About 65 million years ago, the dinosaurs suddenly died out and became extinct. Scientists are still not certain of the reason and over 100 different ideas have been put forward to explain their extinction.

2. The most popular idea is that a meteorite or comet smashed into the Earth. The impact threw up huge clouds of dust which blocked out sunlight for months. As a result the dinosaurs starved and froze to death.

3. Other suggestions include: small mammals eating all the dinosaurs' eggs; dinosaurs growing too big to mate; and being hunted to extinction by aliens in flying saucers!

4. Scientists are also not sure of the timescale of the final extinction. Many dinosaur species had already died out 65 million years ago. The last groups may have been destroyed in as little as an hour, or in as long as 100,000 years!

5. The one thing that scientists do know for sure is that at the end of the dinosaur era it was a mistake to be big! Virtually every creature on the planet that was more than one metre long suddenly died out.

6. Scientists now believe that far from completely disappearing, dinosaurs actually escaped extinction by evolving into birds. Top scientist Professor Ji Qiang has said that modern birds should be thought of as "living feathered dinosaurs"! That means there's probably a dinosaur in your garden right now!